D1302624

TREASURES
OF
BRAZIL

Photography by
Harold and Erica Van Pelt

Cover Photograph
Imperial Topaz crystal and 2 faceted stones from Ouro Preto in Minas Gerais, Brazil.

Designs copyrighted by H.Stern.
All rights reserved. No part of this book may be used, reproduced or transmitted by any means, electronic or mechanical, including translation into other languages, without the written permission from the copyright holder.

Printed in Brazil
ISBN: 85-7390-261-2
9 788573 902617

TREASURES
OF
BRAZIL

H.Stern

The aim of this book is to provide a permanent place for recording noteworthy days and events in your personal life, and in the lives of those dear to you.

It is not intended as an organizer for just one calendar year, but a chronicle to be revised and updated with each passing year, its sturdy binding able to safeguard your entries for future generations.

It is also a book to be treasured, a reference of the fascinating universe of gemstones. Not a collection of technical data, but rather a tool to broaden your knowledge of Brazil's precious stones, illustrated with exquisite photographs.

Use this book to dig deeper into the inviting world of precious minerals. Interesting facts and striking images will enhance your appreciation and shed new light on these much talked-about wonders of nature.

Welcome to it!

H.Stern

When I left my native Germany in 1939, at age 16, to start a new life in Brazil, I had no idea of the magical world I had entered: the vitality of its nature and culture, and the beauty of its precious stones. My fascination with gemstones and their endless variety here compelled me to make these treasures more accessible to the international public.

After a period of apprenticeship as a gem buyer and cutter which took me to the faraway corners of this vast country, I founded H.Stern in 1945. We started small, first trading and cutting gemstones for the wholesale market, and later creating the designs and adding the settings for these wonders of nature by means of skilled goldsmiths in our own workshops, for display to the public in our showrooms and sales outlets.

This policy paid off. We grew by earning the confidence of our clients. Offering them products at fair prices, backed by a unique guarantee and impeccable after-sales service, allowed us to expand. Today we have 160 stores in 12 countries. Branding has made H.Stern a global catchword. Upscale jewelers who maintain our standards also showcase our creations.

My original passion to find the perfect setting for highlighting each stone's unique beauty has evolved into a complex craft with many talented collaborators. Although we are a family-owned business with almost 3,000 employees, a new professional management team remains faithful to our traditions.

This book is the creation of my oldest son, Roberto. It gives evidence to his dedication to the science of gemology and to his many hours of labor to put it together.

My passion to bring these vibrant, exquisite gemstones to more admirers remains unchanged by time. The magical world that enchanted me at 16 has lost none of its luster.

Hans Stern (1922-2007)
Chairman and Founder

Of the many colors of Brazilian topaz, the rarest and most prized is the variety known in the trade as Imperial topaz. The world's only source of this exquisite gem lies near the colonial city of Ouro Preto, in the state of Minas Gerais, where it was discovered nearly 250 years ago.

The major active mining site today is Capão, which currently produces most of the Imperial Topazes available worldwide. Crystals are found there in weathered topaz-quartz-calcite veins. The privately owned Imperial topaz site, the Capão mine, is a very sophisticated operation. Bulldozers work the base of the pit and load dirt, gravel and gem-bearing ore into mechanized dragscrapers, which haul the material to the top of the hill. At a hydraulic washing station, high-pressure water cannons separate the dirt from the material. The gem-bearing ore undergoes further processing until the final hand-sorting on conveyor belts.

The Capão mine processes about 8,000 tons of dirt and gravel per month to recover 30 kg of Imperial topaz, approximately half of which is facet grade. Capão abides by strict environmental regulations, which include the reclamation of water and soil that have been used in the mining process.

Prof. Antonio Veloso

Master Degree in Geochemistry
Geomorphology and Environment Professor
Brazilian Federal University

JANUARY

1	9
2	10
3	11
4	12
5	13
6	14
7	15
8	16

Imperial topaz was first uncovered almost 250 years ago, with its discovery announced in 1768. The area near the colonial city of Ouro Preto is the world's only source of this remarkable gem. Other varieties of topaz occur more commonly elsewhere in Brazil. With limited production in recent years, demand for Imperial topaz continues to soar.

CAPÃO MINE
The prolific Capão mine, near the colonial city of Ouro Preto, is one of the only sources of Imperial topaz.

JANUARY

17	25
18	26
19	27
20	28
21	29
22	30
23	31
24	

IMPERIAL TOPAZ
Imperial topaz is highly valued for its palette of colors: light yellow, orange-yellow, brownish orange, pinkish orange, reddish orange, orange-red and "sherry" red.

Previous page: A spectacular collection of faceted Imperial topaz shows a variety of hues and tones.

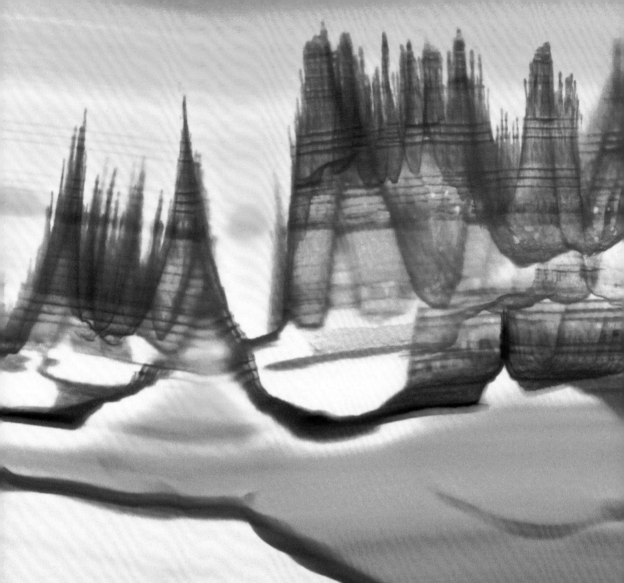

BRAZILIAN AGATE SLICE
This slice of Brazilian agate, a variety
of quartz, reveals a lovely mosaic.

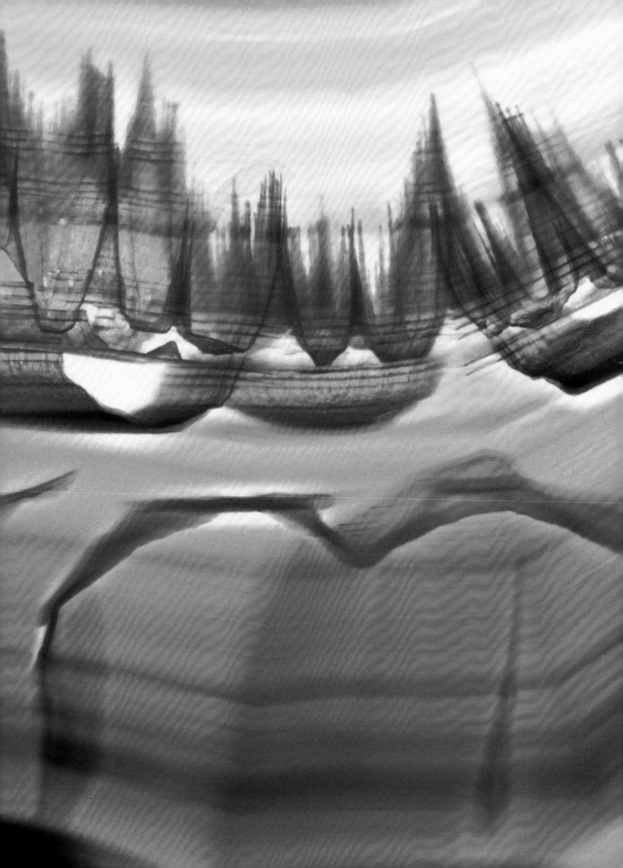

FEBRUARY

1	9
2	10
3	11
4	12
5	13
6	14
7	15
8	16

QUARTZ CLUSTER
The hexagonal structure of double terminated quartz crystals is vividly displayed in this cluster. One of the most common minerals on earth, quartz has been used ornamentally for thousands of years. Quartz grows in a wide range of geologic environments, but crystals require large openings in rocks such as veins, cavities and pockets to grow to full size and perfection.

H.\tern

QUARTZ WITH HEMATITE INCLUSIONS

FEBRUARY

17	25
18	26
19	27
20	28
21	29
22	
23	
24	

QUARTZ WITH INCLUSIONS
In its purest form, quartz is well known as a colorless, transparent rock crystal. Some quartz specimens contain inclusions, minerals trapped within the host crystal that produce artistic images resembling ferns, trees, spangles and even stars. The result is a wonder of nature.

H.Stern

QUARTZ CRYSTALS
Quartz forms in a wide range of geologic environments – hence the variety of quartz gems.

MARCH

1	9
2	10
3	11
4	12
5	13
6	14
7	15
8	16

CITRINE

A heart of fire glistens in the depths of these citrines. A member of the quartz family, citrine ranges in color from rich honey to light lemon yellow. Large, fine citrines are found in several areas of the country, particularly the Serra mine in the state of Rio Grande do Sul. Brazil is the world's primary source of this popular gem.

Following pages: (Left) Citrine's affordability, even in the finest qualities, makes it suitable for one-of-a-kind jewelry pieces. (Right) Honey-toned citrine frosts an 8 cm-high hexagonal crystal set on a glittering drusy crust. In this rare pseudomorph formation, the original mineral – probably beryl – has gradually vanished and been replaced by citrine. Only the outline of the original crystal remains.

H.Stern

MARCH

17	25
18	26
19	27
20	28
21	29
22	30
23	31
24	

FACETED CITRINE
Extraordinarily rich color and exceptional size – 68 carats – make this Brazilian citrine a fine example of quartz family gemstones. The gem's name comes from *citron*, French for "lemon". Iron is the element that gives citrine its distinctively warm color.

RUTILATED QUARTZ SCULPTURE

This stunning abstract gem sculpture
by Bernd Munsteiner stands 20 cm high
on a sterling silver base.
Hand carved from a single crystal of
rutilated quartz, it shows the creative
faceting technique of the total-reflection cut

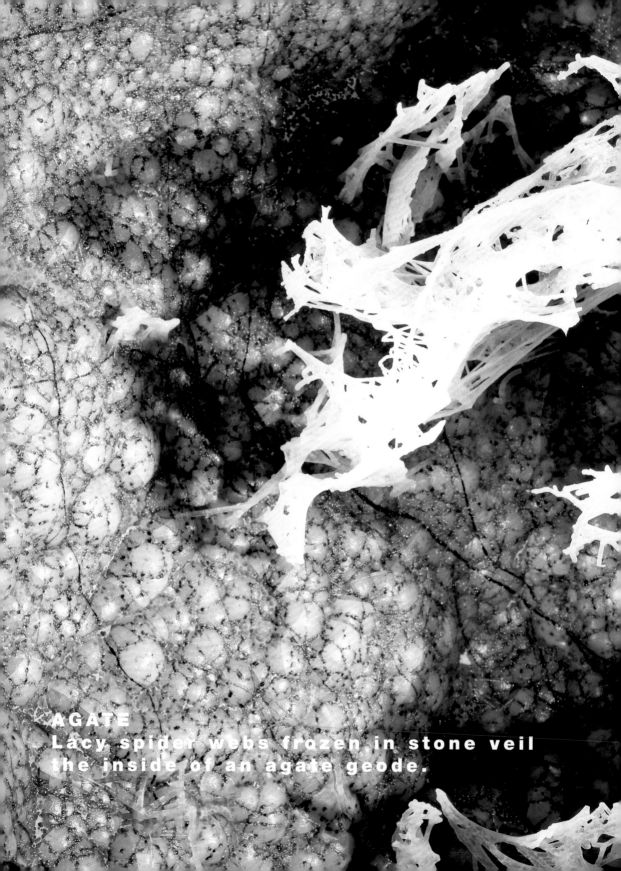

AGATE
Lacy spider webs frozen in stone veil the inside of an agate geode.

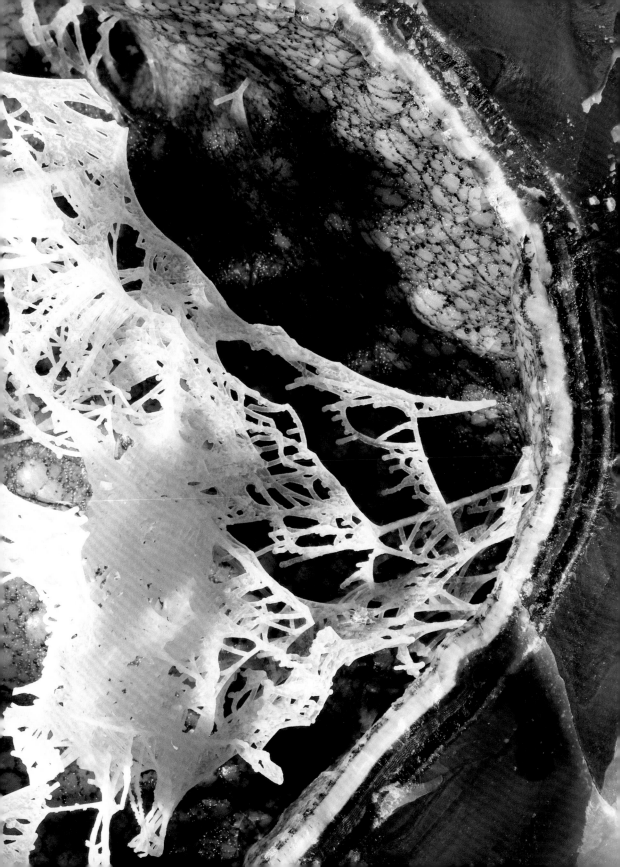

APRIL

1	9
2	10
3	11
4	12
5	13
6	14
7	15
8	16

AMETHYST
A calcite crystal shoots up from an amethyst base in this striking dog-tooth formation. Paler amethysts cluster along its shaft, contrasting with the unusually dark shade of the larger crystal, which stands about 30 cm high.

Following pages: (Left) An amethyst stalactite covered with crystals. (Right) Amethyst is available in a wide assortment of sizes and cuts, including many fancy shapes.

H.Stern

APRIL

17	25
18	26
19	27
20	28
21	29
22	30
23	
24	

AMETHYST
This pale lilac to rich purple gem has long been the most treasured member of the quartz family - hardly a surprise, since purple is the traditional color of royalty. Beautiful yet affordably priced, amethyst is a mainstay of the jewelry industry. Although it is abundant in many parts of the world, some of the finest amethyst comes from Brazil.

AMETHYST STALACTITE SLICE
Like much of the world's amethyst, this stalactite slice with banded agate in the center comes from Brazil.

MAY

1	9
2	10
3	11
4	12
5	13
6	14
7	15
8	16

TOURMALINE

Because of its complex chemical composition, the tourmaline group occurs in a breathtaking range of colors. Its dazzling palette includes greens (the most appreciated color), pinks, reds, yellows, oranges and blues. The H.Stern headquarters in Rio de Janeiro features a display with more then 1,000 samples, one of the most complete tourmaline collections in the world, which were accumulated over 40 years.

H.Stern

TOURMALINE
Rich green tourmaline crystals rise from a feldspar base. Its unusual size - 15cm high - makes this cluster a geological marvel. This piece was found at Araçuaí, in Minas Gerais.

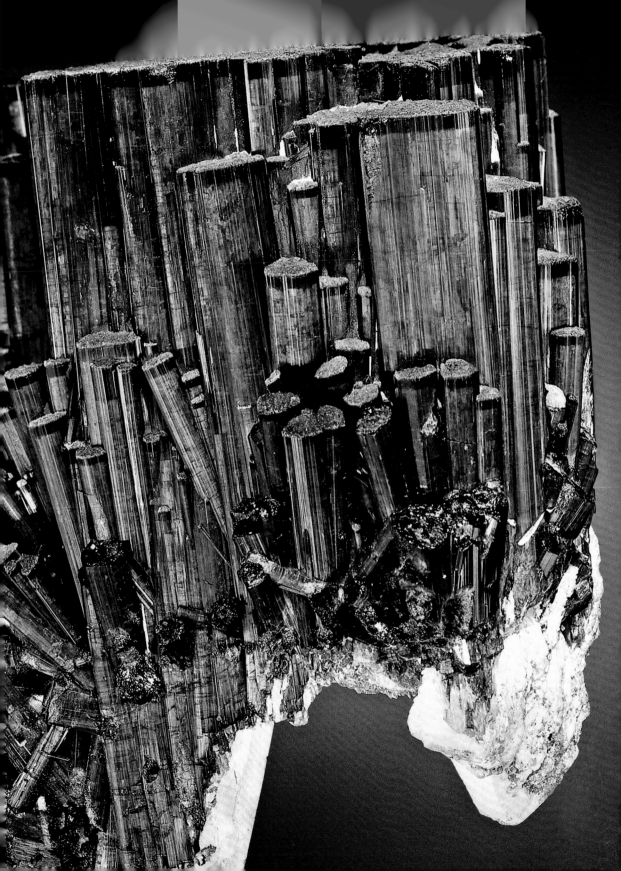

MAY

17	25
18	26
19	27
20	28
21	29
22	30
23	31
24	

JONAS POCKET

The pink to ruby-red variety of the colorful tourmaline group is known as rubellite. In 1978, after six months of unsuccessful digging, an extraordinary pocket of this gem was uncovered at the Jonas mine in southern Minas Gerais. Projecting from the walls of the vast pocket were tons of the largest rubellite crystals ever found. Although the Jonas mine is now abandoned, other sites in Minas Gerais continue to supply fine, cranberry red rubellite.

Following pages: Following pages: (Left) Since the discovery of the very first tourmaline in Brazil in the mid-1500's, the country has been the world's richest source of this colorful gem. High-quality tourmalines have been mined in northeastern Minas Gerais, the heart of the country's gem-mining activity. (Right) The Poquim tourmaline mine, located about 30 km south of Teófilo Otoni in Minas Gerais, has been in operation since 1908. The age-old pick and shovel method is still used at the mine.

H\tern

JUNE

1	9
2	10
3	11
4	12
5	13
6	14
7	15
8	16

BI-COLOR TOURMALINE SCEPTER
Combinations of two or more colors often appear within the same tourmaline crystal. This extraordinary bi-color crystal, narrower at the base than at the top, is known as a scepter.

Following pages: (Left) Weighing 69.80 carats, this rare four-color tourmaline varies in shade from green to white to pink to indigo. The colors in tourmaline appear darkest when viewed along the length of the crystal, with greens and blues appearing almost black. To produce the best color, the cutter must orient the rough crystal correctly before he begins faceting. (Right) A bi-color tourmaline scepter is shown with two faceted tourmalines. The rubellite is a prime example of the cranberry red version of tourmaline. The green tourmaline, known as verdolite, owes its color to traces of iron and titanium.

H\tern

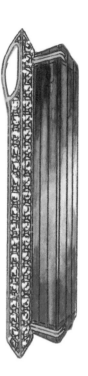

JUNE

17	25
18	26
19	27
20	28
21	29
22	30
23	
24	

PARAÍBA TOURMALINE
A historic tourmaline discovery was made in 1987 in the Brazilian state of Paraíba. The violet, blue and green colors of the tourmalines uncovered at the Mina da Batalha were so intense that they could only be described as "neon" or "electric." Paraíba tourmalines instantly became legendary, attracting enormous demand and commanding prices that were previously unheard of for tourmaline. This extremely rare gem owes its unique color to copper and manganese, a combination of elements that is not found in the other varieties of the gem.

H.Stern

JULY

1	9
2	10
3	11
4	12
5	13
6	14
7	15
8	16

BERYL
Although emerald is the best-known member of the beryl species, this family also boasts several other prized gems, including the sea-blue aquamarine and sun-yellow heliodor shown here. Giant beryl crystals can produce stunningly large gemstones that are virtually flawless. One of the foremost sources of top-quality beryl, Brazil contains vast areas of gem-bearing pegmatite that are still largely unexplored.

H\tern

AQUAMARINE
Fine aquamarine reflects the shades of the sea, making this one of the most attractive gemstones.

JULY

17	25
18	26
19	27
20	28
21	29
22	30
23	31
24	

AQUAMARINE

A member of the beryl family, aquamarine ranges in color from light sky blue to a deep ocean blue. Aquamarine's excellent clarity and brilliance and even color distribution make it a favorite among jewelry designers. Brazil has been the world's most important supplier since 1811, when one of the first aquamarines ever recorded was found in a riverbed near Teofilo Otoni. The world's finest aquamarine continues to come from the pegmatites of northeastern Minas Gerais. Skillfully faceted to take full advantage of their color, this glittering array of aquamarines features cuts that range from antique, pear and step to octagonal, oval, emerald, cushion and marquise.

Following pages: (Left) Outstanding color makes this 32.50 carat hexagonal-cut aquamarine an exquisite beauty. (Right) Top-quality aquamarine lends itself to a wide variety of shapes. Aquamarine crystals are six-sided; like all beryls, they are prismatic, with a hexagonal face at each end of the crystal.

AUGUST

1	9
2	10
3	11
4	12
5	13
6	14
7	15
8	16

EMERALD

Emerald, the deep green variety of beryl, has always carried a singular mystique. While there are many other green gems, emerald is the one universally associated with the color green. Most gem-quality emeralds – including this magnificent 1.66 carat faceted stone and exceptional 3 cm crystal – come from South America, specifically Colombia and Brazil. Depending on the saturation of its color, emeralds can exceed even diamonds in per-carat value.

EMERALD EARRINGS
One of Cleopatra's favorite adornments,
emeralds were mined in Egypt as long
ago as 3000 B.C.

AUGUST

17	25
18	26
19	27
20	28
21	29
22	30
23	31
24	

ROUGH BRAZILIAN EMERALD CRYSTALS
Since 1980 Brazil has become one of the world's most important sources of fine-color emeralds, with the emergence of sites such as Itabira and Capoeirana (Minas Gerais) and Santa Terezinha de Goiás (Goiás state). Brazilian emeralds are unique in that they are colored by trace amounts of vanadium rather than chromium. They are mostly yellow green and often contain fewer inclusions than their Colombian counterparts.

Previous pages: (Left) Large faceted emeralds, weighing 4 to 18 carats, are displayed against a rendering of an emerald necklace. (Right) A rough emerald specimen with white calcite crystals in matrix.

MUZO
The Muzo mine is one of the most famous sources of fine emeralds. Emeralds have been mined in South America since long before explorers arrived in the New World.

SEPTEMBER

1	9
2	10
3	11
4	12
5	13
6	14
7	15
8	16

BLUE TOPAZ

Topaz occurs in an array of colors, and one of the most popular is Blue Topaz, found in the gem-bearing pegmatites of Minas Gerais, possesses a fine, steely luster. This 21 cm high blue topaz crystal, with its wreath of lepidolite, is from the Virgem de Lapa area of Minas Gerais.

Following pages: Blue topaz is one of the most popular gemstones due to its clarity, durability and affordability. (Left) A blue topaz crystal specimen, set in a mica matrix. (Right) An assortment of faceted blue topaz demonstrates the gem's fine luster.

H.Stern

SEPTEMBER

17	25
18	26
19	27
20	28
21	29
22	30
23	
24	

CAT'S-EYE CHRYSOBERYL
Chrysoberyl is among the hardest gemstones, surpassed only by diamond and corundum. The cat's-eye variety of chrysoberyl displays a single white streak down its center. This effect, called *chatoyancy,* is caused by the reflection of light from fine, parallel fibers in a cabochon-cut gem. The eye should open widely in oblique illumination and close sharply in direct illumination. Cat's-eye chrysoberyl has a honey yellow or honey brown to greenish color.

TWINNED CHRYSOBERYL CRYSTAL
Twinning, the symmetrical
intergrowth of two or more
crystals of the same substance,
is common in chrysoberyl.

OCTOBER

1	9
2	10
3	11
4	12
5	13
6	14
7	15
8	16

COLLECTOR STONES
Exceptionally fine gems swirl through the spectrum in a rare display of superb color and sparkling clarity, all cut with expert skill by the lapidaries of H.Stern. Clockwise from center top: topaz, peridot, aquamarine, Imperial topaz, tourmaline, tanzanite, rubellite, blue topaz, andalusite, indicolite (blue tourmaline), and Imperial topaz. In the center are kunzite and, below, heliodor.

Preceding pages: (Left) Located 100 km north of Teófilo Otoni, Minas Gerais, the chrysoberyl mine at Padre Paraíso has produced some exceptional cat's-eye chrysoberyls. (Right) The color-change variety of chrysoberyl, alexandrite appears green or bluish green in daylight and light red in incandescent light. In 1987, a major deposit discovered in Minas Gerais eclipsed all other modern deposits in the size, quality and volume of rare alexandrites it produced.

  H.Stern

OPAL
With its kaleidoscopic play-of-color, precious opal has always been one of the most intriguing gems. Brazil has emerged in recent years as a source of uniquely colored opal, including white, green and blue varieties.

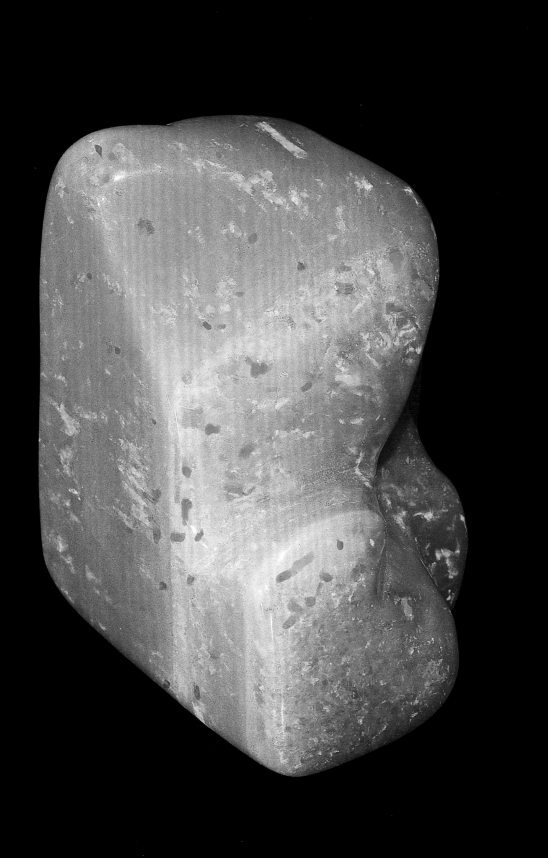

OCTOBER

17	25
18	26
19	27
20	28
21	29
22	30
23	31
24	

RUTILE
Far from being "flaws," mineral inclusions can often add beauty and value to a gem. Rutile is a common mineral inclusion that forms in quartz as sparkling gold and red needle-like strands. These fibers are suspended in the quartz's transparent depths in dramatic patterns, no two alike. Brazil is the world's premier supplier of fine quartz.

RUTILE ON HEMATITE

Rutile on hematite makes up this striking crystal cluster. As useful as they are ornamental, both are industrial ores. Rutile is a rich source of titanium, while hematite provides much of the world's iron.

NOVEMBER

1	9
2	10
3	11
4	12
5	13
6	14
7	15
8	16

KUNZITE

Kunzite is the lavender variety of the mineral spodumene. The gem is named after George Frederick Kunz, the legendary U.S. gemologist who first identified it in southern California in 1902. Today, large kunzite crystals are found in the gem-rich pegmatites of Minas Gerais in lilac, pinkish or violet shades. Although kunzite is not familiar to most consumers, its light, delicate color makes it an attractive choice for gem connoisseurs.

H.Stern

MINE TUNNEL
Coarse-grained granitic rocks known
as pegmatites are among the most
abundant sources of precious gems.
For over 400 years, the pegmatite
deposits of Minas Gerais have yielded
millions of carats of the world's most

NOVEMBER

17	25
18	26
19	27
20	28
21	29
22	30
23	
24	

DIAMOND

Uncut diamond crystals orbit a spectacular full-cut white diamond, the ultimate symbol of eternal love. In addition to its unsurpassed array of colored gemstones, Brazil is also one of the world's oldest sources of diamonds. For more than a century, from the 1720s until the 1870s, Brazil produced many of the world's diamonds. Today, Brazil's newly discovered diamond deposits fuel the dreams of thousands of "garimpeiros", the independent prospectors who form the backbone of the country's mining activity.

Following pages: (Left) This colorless diamond, cut by H.Stern, is a spellbinding design that maximizes the stone's fire and brilliance. (Right) Though often thought of as colorless, diamonds are found in all colors. Those with good color, such as these marquise-cut diamonds, are exceptional treasures.

STERN STAR ®
H.Stern 2011

DECEMBER

1	9
2	10
3	11
4	12
5	13
6	14
7	15
8	16

IMPERIAL CROWN

Located an hour outside of Rio de Janeiro is the royal city of Petropolis, once the summer home of Brazil's imperial family. Their former palace, which has since been converted into a museum, now houses the Imperial Crown. The crown was made for Emperor Pedro I in the early 19th century and later passed along to Pedro II, the last monarch to rule the country. This magnificent gold treasure weighs nearly 2 kg and is encrusted with 639 Brazilian diamonds and 77 pearls. For centuries, Brazilian diamonds have adorned royalty around the world, and H.Stern is proud to have been entrusted by the museum's curators to restore this crown to its original brilliance.

H.Stern

BRAZILIAN GOLD SPECIMEN

DECEMBER

17	25
18	26
19	27
20	28
21	29
22	30
23	31
24	

VARIOUS CUTS
This assortment of colored gemstones from Brazil shows a variety of popular cuts that are used to maximize the color and brilliance of these natural treasures.

Preceding pages: The most precious metal through the ages, gold's malleability, durability and sheer beauty make it a perfect metal for mounting diamonds and colored gemstones. In the past two decades, Brazil has become one of the world's largest gold producers as new finds have emerged.

(Left) The age-old art of lapidary gives light and life to Nature's geological masterpieces. Produced over millennia by massive forces at work in the earth's crust, gemstones are simply raw materials until the craftsman's hand brings their beauty to its final finish, with his hard-earned knowledge of shaping, cutting, faceting and polishing. Master craftsmen may spend up to ten years in the H.Stern lapidary workshops before being given the responsibility of cutting important stones.
(Right) The design team at the H.Stern studios provides the creative inspiration for unforgettable masterpieces of fine jewelry.

AGATE GEODES
Agate geodes appear to be ordinary
rocks from the outside, but when cut
open they reveal a beautiful display of
color and design.

Brazil is a land of unsurpassed gem wealth.
For centuries, the southeastern state of Minas
Gerais ("General Mines") has been the center
of Brazil's gem mining activity.
Portuguese explorers first discovered gem
deposits in this mountainous region in the late
16th century, and organized mining has taken
place there since the early 1800's.
Throughout Minas Gerais important deposits
of beryl, chrysoberyl, topaz, tourmaline and
quartz, in practically every color of the
spectrum can be found.

GEM PEGMATITE MINES OF MINAS GERAIS

● *Beryl*   ● *Kunzite*   ● *Chrysoberyl*   ● *Tourmaline*

●BG Baixa Grande	●P-TB-U Pioneer-Três Barras-Urubu
●BC Barra de Cuieté	●Q Quarto Centenario
●B Barra de Salinas	●S Salinas
●CB Corrego Barro	●SOL Santa Rita-Olho d'Agua-Lufas
Preto & Gil	●SR Santa Rosa
●C Cruzeiro-Aricanga	●Sa Sapucaia
●FF Fazenda do Funil	●T Toca de Onca
●FL Fortaleza	●Uc Urucum
●F Frade-Coronel Murta	●Up Urupuca
●G Golconda	●X Xanda
●HI Happy Island	
●JE Jenipapo	
●J Jonas-Cascalho	
●La Laranjeiras	
●LV Lavrinha	
●L Limoeiro	
●MM Manoel Mutuca	
●M-C Mercello-Chia	
●MR Marta Rocha	
●Mx Maxixe	
●Me Medina	
●Ub Mina Urubu	
●M Morro Redondo	
●Mu Mucaia-Murundu	
●OF Ouro Fino-Lorena	
●P Papamel	
●P-P Piauí-Pirineus	

H\tern

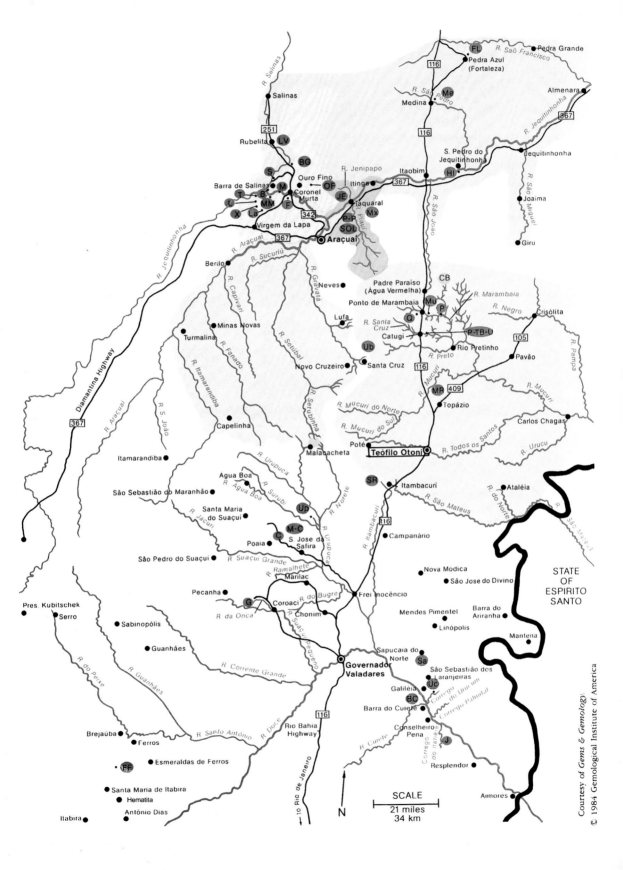

R. Salinas

• Salinas

FL

R. São Francisco

• Pedra Grande

116

• Pedra Azul
(Fortaleza)

• Almenara

R. São Pedro

Me

Medina

116

R. Jequitinhonha

367

251

Rubelita

LV

• S. Pedro do
Jequitinhonha

HI

• Jequitinhonha

R. São Miguel

BG

R. Jenipapo

Itaobim

S

Ouro Fino

OF

• Joaima

Barra de Salinas

M

Coronel
Murta

Ittinga

367

T   B

JE

• Giru

L   MM

Taquaral

Mx

R. São João

X   La   F

P-P

SOL

Virgem da Lapa

342

Araçuaí

367

R. Araçuaí

R. Sucuriú

Berilo

R. Gravatá

Padre Paraíso
(Água Vermelha)

CB

• Neves

R. Marambaia

Ponto de Marambaia

Mu

R. Negro

• Crisólita

R. Capivari

Lufa

Q

P

P-TB-U

105

R. Pampa

• Minas Novas

R. Santa
Cruz

Catugi

Ub

• Rio Pretinho

R. Setúbal

Turmalina

R. Fanado

Novo Cruzeiro

• Santa Cruz

116

R. Preto

• Pavão

Diamantina Highway

R. Araçuaí

R. S. João

R. Itamarandiba

Capelinha

MR

409

Topázio

R. Mucuri

R. Mucuri do Norte

• Carlos Chagas

R. Serubinha

R. Mucuri do Sul

367

• Itamarandiba

R. Urupuca

Malacacheta

Poté

R. Todos os Santos

R. Urucu

Teófilo Otoni

Agua Boa

R. Agua Boa

R. Surubi

SR

• Itambacuri

• Atálaia

R. do Norte

São Sebastião do Maranhão

R. Jacuri

Up

R. Norete

116

R. São Mateus

R. São Mateus

STATE
OF
ESPÍRITO
SANTO

Santa Maria
do Suaçuí

M-C

R. Itambacuri

• Campanário

Poaia

C

S. Jose da
Safira

São Pedro do Suaçuí

R. Suaçuí Grande

R. Ramalhete

• Nova Modica

• São Jose do Divino

Pres. Kubitschek

Marilac

Pecanha

G

Coroaci

R. do Bugre

Frei Inocêncio

Mendes Pimentel

Barra do
Ariranha

• Serro

R. da Onça

Chonim

• Linópolis

• Mantena

• Sabinópolis

R. Suaçuí Pequeno

• Guanhães

R. Corrente Grande

Governador
Valadares

Sapucaia do
Norte

Sa

São Sebastião dos
Laranjeiras

Uc

Córrego do Urucum

R. do Peixe

R. Guanhães

R. Santo Antônio

R. Doce

Galiléia

BC

Córrego Palmital

Barra do Cuieté

• Brejaúba

• Ferros

Rio Bahia
Highway

R. Cuieté

Conselheiro
Pena

Córrego da Natividade

J

FF

• Esmeraldas de Ferros

To Rio de Janeiro

• Resplendor

• Santa Maria de Itabira

• Hematita

SCALE

• Itabira

• Antônio Dias

N

21 miles
34 km

• Aimorés

Courtesy of Gems & Gemology.
© 1984 Gemological Institute of America

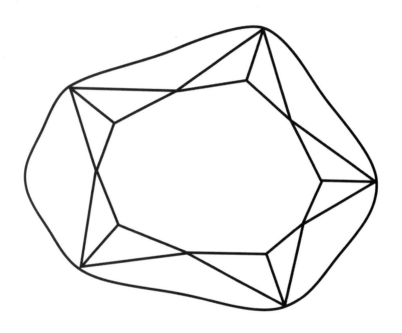

STERN STAR ®
H.Stern 2011